BORN TO GIGGLE!

A COLLECTION OF POEMS FOR CHILDREN

Edited by Ian Billings and Hunt Emerson

Published by

 Save the Children

Born To Giggle!
A Collection of Poems for Children.
Edited by Ian Billings and Hunt Emerson
Published by Save the Children.
1 St. John's Lane, London, EC1M 4AR
This collection © 2012 Save the Children
All poems and drawings are © the respective creators.

All profits from the sale of this book will help children
here in the UK and in 120 countries around the world.

ISBN: 978 1 84187 129 5

BORN TO GIGGLE!

Hello!

In your hand is the greatest collection of children's poets ever herded together in one spot. Poets of all shapes, sizes, ages and heights. We've been coaxing, cajoling and pestering them for months to hand over a poem or two for a good cause and the results are right here before your eyes, ears and nose.

Plunge in at any point and grab a giggle or, take a deep breath, and wade through the entire lot in one gulp. It's up to you. But remember every time you chuckle, giggle, guffaw or chortle you're doing it for charity! That makes you a good person. Well done. Pat yourself on the head – or get a grown-up to do it.

Thanks to everyone who put pen to paper, finger to keyboard and ear to phone to make this happen! We've had a hoot putting it all together – so if you enjoy the book tell all your friends. If you haven't just keep it to yourself, okay?

Now stop reading this introduction and get giggling!

Ian Billings

Ian hasn't mentioned the talented and generous gang of cartoonists who have given us a great set of cartoons to go with the poems. Thanks to all of them too - may your lines be ever wobbly!

Hunt Emerson

THE CARTOONISTS

Andrew Chiu
Brick
Cat Reda
Chris White
Clive Goddard
Ellie Cummins
Gemma Sheldrake
Graham Higgins
Hunt Emerson
Jane McGuinness
John Crawford
John McCrea
Laura Howell
Mikey B

Nathan Ariss
Noel Ford
Philip Waddell
Roger Penwill
Ryan Taylor
Sammy Borras
Sarah Fogg
Shaz Jubeen
Simon Woolford
Suzy Varty
The Surreal McCoy
Tim Harries
Tim Leatherbarrow
Will Dawbarn

THE POETS

Chris White
Philip Monks
Justin Coe
John Hegley
Julie Boden
Jane Clarke
Joan McLellan
Paul Cookson
Eric Finney
Ian McMillan
Bernard Young
Brian Patten
Matt Harvey
James Carter
Julia Jarman
Roger Stevens
John Rice
Alan Durant
Ian Billings
Jill Townsend
Steph Dale
Celia Warren
Brian Moses
Fi Gallimore

Joan Lennon
John Foster
Emma Purshouse
Gwen Grant
Philip Waddell
Nick Toczek
Antony Lishak
David Calcutt
John Rice
Jane Clarke
Nick Green
Tony Mitton
Sandra Horn
Paul Dowswell
Enid Richemont
Joan Poulson
Steven Herrick
Trevor Parsons
Terry Caffrey
Gez Walsh
Joe Craig
Alison Chisholm
Wes Magee

Save the Children

Around the world thousands of children are dying unnecessarily every day and Save the Children believe this is totally unacceptable.

Join us in our campaign - **'No Child Born To Die'**

No child is born to die from not having enough food,
No child is born to die from drinking dirty water,
No child is born to die from a mosquito bite,
No child is born to die from a tummy bug.

No child is born to die.

Every child is born to sing,
born to dance,
born to play
and **every** child is born to giggle...

By buying this book you will help Save the Children
ensure that no child is born to die
and every child is born to shine.

Thank you from everyone at Save the Children.

If you would like to do more to help children here in the UK and in the 120 countries where we work, then please contact us at **volunteersupport@savethechildren.org.uk** or ring 0207 012 6997.
www.savethechildren.org.uk
Registered charity England and Wales (213890)
Scotland (SC039570)

SAVE A...

There are many creatures on this planet of ours,
That help us everyday.
Working to please the Human Race,
Each in their small way.

And, y'know, what thanks do they get?
None – for goodness sake!
So I'm saying to you – let's change what we do
And give some animals a break!

People ride horses all the time,
Up and down this great nation.
Here's an idea for you! Try something new!
And save a horse – ride an Alsatian!

How about cows? Daily giving their milk,
Without any thanks or merit.
We'll find a new way! Give 'em a holiday!
And save a cow – milk a ferret!

Just think of the ducks whose feathers are stuck
Into pillows for your sleepy head.
Well, listen up dude – help them stop being nude!
Save a duck - pluck a budgie instead!

What of the sheep? Sacrificing their wool,
To make a new coat or a hat.
All over the nation – give them a vacation.
And save a sheep – sheer a cat!!

For some people, to swim with dolphins,
Is all they've wanted from the day they were born.
The poor things need a rest! I'll tell you what's best!
Save a dolphin – swim with a prawn!

Humans use mighty elephants to move
Heavy things with their strength and their power.
Well, hey, what about letting them just chill out?
Save an elephant – load up a chihuahua!

And of course, helping Save the Children
Is something we all can do.
And, guess what? Today, you've helped in a big way
By buying this book, so thank you!

Poem and drawing by **Chris White**

THE COMMAS ARE COMING

The commas are coming, watch out, watch out.
They wriggle, they writhe, they slither about.
Just when you think that you are okay,
along comes a comma, to sweep you away.

They make you pause, that's what they do,
and if you're not careful, they're all over you.
So do not stutter, when you utter,
do take care, and be aware,
wherever the words are, commas are there.

I once met a girl who tried to escape from them and she
thought that if she could
keep going long enough she would make a break from
them but in the end it was stupid because her
sentences were all jumbled up and she
             finally
had to admit that she had completely run out of puff.

Commas, strong stuff.

I once knew a boy who tried to defy the comma.
His sentences were short. On my honour.
He was happy. Sort of. I knew it wouldn't last.
Short sentences are quick.
Short sentences are fast.
But they are bit boring.
You get a bit sick of them.
You get to ignoring them.

They're all a bit the same.
It's not much of a game.
And there's not much of a trick to them.
I knew that boy would be a goner
when he saw the wriggling, writhing, interesting, string-
it-along, keep it moving, keep it grooving, get on down,
singing, dancing, all-entrancing, good at describing
commas.

Sure enough,
one day
The commas came.
They were as hot as summer's sand,
they were slippy, slippy as the sea,
they were wild, wild as the white, foaming waves.

They started to dance, and the dance got faster, and
faster,
until that boy knew,
I'm telling you,
his was a comma disaster.

He started to dance the swirling, curling, dance of the
commas.
No more comma-less sentences.
Except in emergencies.
He wanted to describe, how shall I put it, the cleverness
of things.
He wanted to say, for example, if they were blue, or
gold, or green.
I want to say, he explained, exactly what I mean.
Come on, said the comma, here's your chance.
And he took it, no contest.
It was, I think you'll agree, all for the best.

So, come on, join in.
The commas are fun.
Wriggle and jiggle and comma it up.
The water's lovely, if you fancy a dip.

Enjoy your commas, and your pauses,
and get on down to those subordinate clauses.

- Philip Monks

POET IN SCHOOLS

He thought the kids would find his verse boring
But strangely they laughed through each one
He hoped it was 'cos the poems were good
And not 'cos his flies were undone

- Justin Coe

WISE CAMEL

I'm the beast
that bore
wise man number four
We're the ones who went North
when the others went West
We followed, not the Star of David
but the star of Steve.

My rider wasn't sure that his gift was as good
as the other three.
I sometimes wonder
If we got lost on purpose.
Myself, I thought
he brought the best of the gifts, actually:
the gift of straw,
the gift of warmth.
Warmth for the manger
But because he wasn't sure
his gift was good enough
he kept adding straw
It was the last one that did it
So I'm on the wrong track
with busted back
but luckily we found this town with a really good vet
And, in the end,
had a pleasant, if rather quiet, Christmas

*- **John Hegley***   *Drawing - **Roger Penwill***

DON'T SWAT THE FLY, DAD!

Don't swat the fly, Dad,
don't bash the bug,
don't smash the spider
or give its web a tug.
Don't asphyxiate the ants.
Don't crush the centipede.
It took all day to tie each shoe.
The last thing he will need
is to be squashed, Dad,
by the giant shoe
of
You

- Julie Boden   *Drawing -Jane McGuiness*

A DROP IN THE OCEAN

Sploshing around
in life's restless sea,
there's a drop in the ocean -
and that drop is me.

Surfing the waves,
or washed up on the shore,
I'm a minuscule drop
amongst zillions more.

I'm a drop in the ocean
of life's restless sea -
but there'd be no ocean
without drops like me!

- Jane Clarke   *Drawing - **Gemma Sheldrake***

OH WHY DOES MY DOG LOOK SO SAD?

Oh, why does my dog look so sad?
That look's really sending me mad.
Those two giant eyes just stare up at me,
Glazed and unblinking, all doleful and glum
I've got to do something to cheer up my chum.
I know what he needs; a real long fast run
Through scent laden woods, just out having fun.

Oh, why does my dog look so sad?
That look's really sending me mad.
Those eyes have grown bigger, I'm sure they have.
That shiny black nose points the way to the door
As he lies stretched out flat with his chin on the floor.
I know what he needs; a real tasty lunch
With huge chunks of meat or bones full of crunch.

Oh, why does my dog look so sad?
That look's really sending me mad.
Now his eyes are shut tight and he won't look at me.
Then the deepest of sighs tells me life is a bore,
And to ram home his point he lets out a snore.
I know what he needs; a real frantic game;
To race and to run, where stopping's a shame.

Is that really a smile or a line crinkled frown?
Is he happy with me? Can I finally sit down?
So I flop with great relish in my old comfy chair,
Then, his eyes lock on tight to the dog-nibbly shelf.
While I follow his gaze, I say to myself
Wait a mo' silly, just who's training who?
And I race to the kitchen to fetch him a chew.

*– **Joan McLellan***   *Drawing - **Simon Woolford***

BATH WATERS RUN DEEP

Dad did not smile nor did he laugh
Seeing the shark fin in the bath
Instead, began to fuss and fuss
When tickled by the octopus
His eyes could not believe it real
The shock of the electric eel
And then up popped the toilet lid
Shooting out a giant squid

His arms and legs began to flail
Until he saw the killer whale
He sat stock still, too scared to move
The swordfish had a point to prove
It did so with a sharpened swish
And then dad saw the jellyfish
That shivered, shook and grew and grew
So dad began to shiver too

That was the least of current troubles
When bursting upwards through the bubbles
A mile of oily coils and – yes,
It was the monster from Loch Ness!
Dad wished he washed in just the sink
Bath water's deeper than you think
He also wished – and this is rude
He was not bathing in the nude

And since he was, his final wish
Was not to see pirhana fish
Alas, these wishes don't come true
Pirhana fish swam into view
A thousand spiky snapping teeth
That started biting underneath
A starfish then joined in the fun
At this point dad began to run

So out he leapt with piercing howl
But could not find a single towel
A blur of pink and he was gone
Crabs and lobsters hanging on
So when you have a bath take care
Of monsters lurking everywhere
The moral of this tale will be
It's safer bathing in the sea!

– Paul Cookson   *Drawing* **- The Surreal McCoy**

PRONTOFAURUS

I called to a halt our tiny band
Of time-travelling explaurus
And now we crouched behind some rocks
Amazed at the scene befaurus.
Surely that majestic beast
Was the great tyrannosaurus
And there, close by, with thunderous cry
Lumbered a brontosaurus.
We rubbed our eyes – it was indeed
A sight to overaurus.
Just then they raised their mighty heads
In a blood-curdling chaurus,
Led, if my eyes did not deceive,
By a huge brachiosaurus.
I wondered just how long these beasts
Would continue to ignaurus . . .

No sooner had I had this thought
Than it was plain – they saurus!
And to our horror, in stampede,
Headed directly faurus.
It was their clear intention
To paurus and to claurus
And one horned monster obviously
Would surely try to gaurus.
"It would be wise, sir," one man breathed,
"At this point to withdraurus."
So, "Back to the chopper, folks!" I cried,
"Come on, it's prontofaurus!"
Safely aloft and much relieved
We sipped cocoa to restaurus.

[Spelling errors in this poem –
You'll easily detect them –
Are just included to amuse.
Of course, you could correct them . . .]

- Eric Finney   *Drawing -* **Hunt Emerson**

I LIKE A WOOD

I've got to confess I like a glade;
A tent made of leaves, a tree-shelter,
Somewhere to sit in the afternoon shade
And say, quietly,
        I do like a glade.

I've got to confess I like a copse;
A branch of a twig office, a root-shed
Somewhere to sit where time just stops
And say, slowly,
        I do like a copse.

I've got to confess I like a wood;
A trunk-palace, a bird-street
Somewhere to sit that's fulfilling, complete,
And say, happily,
        I do like a wood.

- Ian McMillan   *Drawing -* **Sarah Fogg**

BEST FRIENDS

Would a best friend
      Eat your last sweet
      Talk about you behind your back
      Have a party and not ask you?
Mine did.

Would a best friend
      Borrow your bike without telling you
      Deliberately forget your birthday
      Avoid you whenever possible?
Mine did.

Would a best friend
      Turn up on your bike
      Give you a whole packet of your favourite sweets
      Look you in the eye?
Mine did.

Would a best friend say
      Sorry I talked about you behind your back
      Sorry I had a party and didn't invite you
      Sorry I deliberately forgot your birthday
      - I thought you'd fallen out with me
Mine did.

      And would a best friend say, simply,
      Never mind
      That's OK
I did

- Bernard Young

REBELLION ON THE CATWALK

The snake-skin hissed, 'I hate this show!'
The leopard-skin said it did too.
The fox-fur said, 'I concur.
I'm leaving, how about you?'
The clothes the crowd had been wearing
Cried out, 'Enough is enough!
We never wore human skin –
We could do without that stuff.'
The clothes struggled free of their captors,
There was a sudden uproar
As with revitalised grins the fur-coats and the skins
Rushed out of the exit door.
The audience were astonished.
They were left half-naked and cold –
The young, the fat, the flabby,
The tall, the skinny, the old.
'My leather trousers are gone!
I feel silly and chilly!
I've only my hat left
To cover my willy!'
'Where's my leopard-skin dress?
My bra looks a mess!
Please turn away,
My knickers are grey!'
There was quite a commotion,
Everyone felt such a fool,
Except a young usherette in a nice
cotton dress
Who said, 'I couldn't care less,
Killing for fashion is cruel.'

- Brian Patten

CUSTER'S LAST LAUGH

Ha ha ha ha ha ha
Ha ha ha ha
He he he
Ha ha
Haaaaa
      aaa
        aaarr
          rrgg
            gghh

urgle
gurgle

spleuchhh

- Matt Harvey   *Drawing - Tim Leatherbarrow*

BUCKET!

Bucket full of seashells
bucket full of sea
bucket full of creatures
one-two-three!
Bucket full of seaweed
bucket full of sun
bucket full of memories
bucket full of fun!
Bucket full of holiday
bucket full of sand
bucket full of happiness
in my hand!

- James Carter   *Drawing - Suzy Varty*

SMELLY NELLY

There was a girl who wouldn't wash.
She didn't like the splish and splosh
Of water in the bath or sink.
She only liked what made her stink!

Smelly Nelly was her name,
A fearful pong her claim to fame.
She hated soap, she loathed shampoo.
Her Mother didn't know what to do.

She wouldn't wash; she wouldn't shower
Though Mother begged her by the hour.
"Smelly Nelly, have a bath, dear.
Friends and rellies won't come near!"

They thought they might catch lice or fleas
Or some terrible skin disease.
"Smelly Nelly, please wash your hair.
There are bits of food in there."

Nelly said, "I can eat those later.
See, egg, cheese and mashed potat-er."
Mother cried, "Well, brush your teeth.
Your teeth look like a coral reef!

They are sticky with yellow plaque
Your breath is foul, it knocks me back"
But Nelly hated using toothpaste.
She didn't like the minty fresh taste.

Nelly's dad went on the war path.
He ordered Nelly, "Take a bath!
Smelly Nelly, you smell musty.
Smelly Nelly, your skin is crusty.

Smelly Nelly, scrub your nails.
They're grey and black like little snails!"
Nelly's mum burst into tears,
"You could grow carrots in your ears!"

And Father said, "Why stop there?
We could grow cabbages in her hair!
In fact, my dear, that's a good idea!
Dirt can be our Nell's career!

There's a saying - it's quite funny -
Where there's muck, then there's money.
Well, there's profit in all this filth.
Nell is covered in a very fine tilth!"

Dad rushed out and bought some seeds.
Poppies, pansies, peas and swedes.
He set the seeds when he got home.
The soil was good, a very fine loam.

Dad set daisies between Nelly's toes.
And marigolds inside her nose.
He sprinkled poppies along her arms.
Love-in-a-mist in both her palms.

Then he poured manure all over Nelly.
She didn't notice, she was so smelly.
And soon the seeds began to grow.
Till Nelly looked like a flower show!

Some of the flowers smelled quite sweet
And masked the pong of Nelly's feet!
Dad said "The Flower Show's coming up.
Our Nell's a winner. She'll get a cup."

But Nelly yelled, "STOP! I've had enough!
Of dung and dirt and filth and stuff!
I do not like the stink and reek
And people thinking I'm a freak.

I'm going home. I want to wash!"
"Oh no!" said Mum. Her dad cried, "Tosh!"
But Nelly ran home as Dad gave chase
- and Smelly Nelly won the race.

She was jumping in the bath
As her Dad ran up the path.
"Stop!" he yelled, as water flowed downstairs!
But Nelly yelled back, "I'm washing my hair!"

"Well, don't!" yelled her dad, seeing lather.
But Nelly screamed back, "I'm obeying you, father!"
But Dad's love of hygiene had diminished.
He rushed upstairs. "Haven't you finished?"

"No!" laughed Nelly, "I'll never be done
I love the bath, I'm having fun."
She'd discovered the joy of soap.
In bottles and tubes and on a rope.

Splashing and spraying made her laugh
And blowing bubbles in the bath,
And squirting herself with perfumed jelly
So fragrant Nelly stopped being smelly.

Sweet-smelling Nelly now loved washing
Rubbing, scrubbing, splishing and sploshing.
She loved the loofah and the flannel
And pretending to swim the channel!

She loved the bathroom and the shower
She stayed there hour after hour after hour …

In fact I think she's still there now ...

NB If you prefer a more traditional cautionary ending you might like this, but I can't bear it.

All through the summer Nelly bloomed
But when Autumn came the girl was doomed
For the flowers died when the frost set in
And Dad dumped Nelly in the compost bin.

- Julia Jarman   *Drawings - **Clive Goddard***

THE HEDGEHOG AND THE SLOTH

I wandered lonely as a hedgehog
Who saunters through the undergrowth
When all at once I met a frog
In conversation with a sloth
You move so slowly, said the frog
You're almost at a stop
But there's so much to do and see
I'm always on the hop.
Well, said the sloth, and minutes passed
As the sloth chewed on his lip
The frog waited impatiently
And then said, Toodle pip!

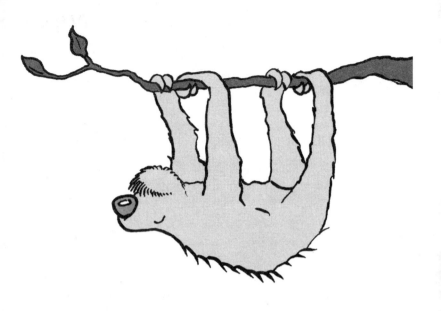

So, said the sloth, eventually
My views I guess you seek
Then thought some more (about half an hour)
Please come back Thursday week
By now, of course, the frog had gone
To chase a dragonfly
And I resumed my wandering
And ate my custard pie

- Roger Stevens   *Drawing - John Crawford*

TV RAP

After school
what suits me
is to sit on the carpet
and watch TV.

Watch TV
Watch TV
I sit on the carpet
and watch TV.

I burst in
about half past three.
Kick off my shoes
and get comfy.

Get comfy
Get comfy
I kick off my shoes
and get comfy.

Dad says, 'You're too near.
Take my advice.
Move further back
or you'll damage your eyes.'

But my eyes don't hurt
and they haven't turned square.
Close to the screen
is what I prefer.

When I get home
what pleases me
is to sit on the carpet
and watch TV.

I watch TV
I watch TV
and I don't budge
until it's time for tea.

Time for tea
Time for tea
I don't budge
until it's time for tea

- Bernard Young
*Drawing - **Will Dawbarn***

SPOILT FOR CHOICE

One fine evening my mother said to me,
"My dear darling Alan, what would you like for tea?
Maybe fish and chips or hot pot?
Spaghetti or macaroni cheese?
Eggs on toast with vinegar?
Sausages with gravy and mushy peas?
Roast pork with mashed potatoes?
Stir fry or spicy chicken curry?
A burger with salad and French fries?
A pizza with slices of pepperoni?
Duck a l'orange, my sweet one?
Steak tartare or cassoulet?
Tasty snails in garlic butter?
Boeuf Bourguignon or jambon fricassee?
My dear darling Alan, tell me,
What would you like for tea?"
And I said, "Jelly."

"Jelly, my dear darling Alan," my mother said to me.
"If jelly it is you really want, then jelly it shall be.
Would you like strawberry jelly or raspberry?
Lemon or lime, orange or gooseberry?
Red jelly, yellow jelly, jelly that's pink or gold?
Jelly shaped like a rabbit from my special jelly mould?
Jelly that wibbles and wobbles, jelly that stands up tall?
Jelly that melts in your mouth, jelly that's warm or cool?
Milk jelly, chocolate jelly, jelly from the deli?
Jelly that's so sweet, it will sing in your belly?
Tell me my dear darling Alan, please tell me, do,
What kind of jelly shall I make for you?"
And I said, "Blue."

"Blue jelly, my dear darling Alan," my mother said to me,
"If blue jelly's what you want, blue jelly it shall be.
I'll make you delicious blue jelly for your tea.
Would you like baby blue or turquoise, royal blue or navy?
The blue of a clear, bright sky or a sea all wild and wavy?
Cyan or aquamarine, midnight blue or duck egg?
Blue like the jeans you wear or the veins running down your leg?
Azure blue or cobalt, air force blue or peacock?
Blue as lapis lazuli or an early summer forget-me-not?
Blue like when you're feeling sad?
Or the spots of mould on food that's bad?
Blue as cornflowers in a field, blue as sparkling sap-phires?
Blue as your fingers in the cold or blue as gas-flame fires?
My dear darling Alan, tell me," my mother said to me,
"What shade of blue jelly would you like for your tea?"
And I said, "Actually, Mum, I think I'll just have a salad."

– Alan Durant

BOUNCY CASTLE

In the Bouncy Castle
Lived the Bouncy King and Queen
And their Bouncy little daughter
Princess Maureen.

They bounced all day
And most of the night
Bounced through the weekend
It was quite a sight.

But Princess Maureen
Soon got bored
And hatched a plan
While her parents snored.

She rummaged around
And found a pin
Went to their bedroom
And bounced quietly in.

Over to the bed
With a bo-ing and a hop
She pricked papa
And pop went pop.

Mama woke and spoke
With a frown
"I think you've let
Your father down!"

"It won't happen again,
I do declare!"
Declared the Princess
But that was all hot-air.

Between you and me
Her chance are blown
Of ever inheriting
The bouncy throne!

- Ian Billings   *Drawing - **Hunt Emerson***

CHEERING MUM UP

I picked a flower for my mum
when she was sad and looking glum.
She smiled as she took the rose
and sniffed some greenfly up her nose.

- Jill Townsend   *Drawing - Tim Harries*

WHAT DID YOU DO AT SCHOOL TODAY?

WhatDidYouDoAtSchoolToday?
Nothing.
Nothing?
Well, nothing much.
You did nothing much all day long?
Well . . . alright Mum, if you really want to know,
I had 4 lessons
and 45 minutes of playtime
in which I went around with 3 friends.
For lunch I had 22 baked beans,
2 fishfingers, a 1/4 of a bread roll
and 1 banana.
I fed Nibbles, the class hamster,
2 sunflower seeds.
I wrote 1 poem.
I got 7/10 for a spelling test.
I did 16 fairly tricky maths questions.
And…I learnt 5 very interesting things
about the Ancient Egyptians, including
how they used to remove the brains
of their dead with a hook - MUM…
DO YOU EVER LISTEN TO A WORD I SAY?
Oh sorry darling, what was that?
I said I removed my teacher's brain today!
What? Oh well done, you!
What would you like for tea?

- James Carter

MY SECRET

Boys spend hours looking at the sky
Wondering what's out there
I prefer to think about my cellar
I know for fact who's down there
He arrived on Tuesday morning
He arrived without a boom or a bang
He just turned up with
a red ball
a letter
a pack of moon dust
in his green little hand.
He asked if I could keep a secret
I said girls could do that.
And so now,
There's an alien in my cellar
In fact he's turned it into a nice little flat.
He doesn't want the publicity
He doesn't want magazine deals
He's quite happy with a small cup of tea
And my roller skates with little pink wheels
He's taking a liking to Trisha
But he doesn't like sleeping in bed
Instead he likes to dance in the garden
With a watering can on his head.
I haven't broken my promise
I've just told you he is there.
But you don't know where I live
So you can't come round and stare.

- Steph Dale

*Drawing - **The Surreal McCoy***

NEVER SIT ON A SQUID

Never sit on a squid
It would squirt if you did
And your shirt would get dirty and stink.

Never sit on a squid
It would squish if you did
And you'd never get rid of the ink.

- Celia Warren　　　　　*Drawing - **Hunt Emerson***

A Good Scary Poem Needs......

A haunted house,

a pattering mouse.

A spooky feeling,

a spider-webbed celing.

A squeaking door,

a creaking floor.

A swooping bat,

the eyes of a cat.

a dreadful dream,

a distant scream.

A ghost that goes '**BOO**'

and **You!**

- Brian Moses

A FEW ZOO HAIKU

African Painted Hunting Dogs

Giant paint-splotched ears
        rising up out of the grass
           glad I'm not dinner!

Pygmy Marmoset

So incredibly
        tiny - how do you fit all
           your insides inside?

Greedy Chimp

That chimpanzee can't
      walk – all his feet are too full
        of bright green apples

Some of the things we didn't do at the zoo …

      High-jacked the zebra
        bus - tickled tapirs - painted
          boy flamingos blue!

– Joan Lennon   *Drawings - Graham Higgins*

HAVE YOU EVER?

Have you ever seen a fox learning how to box
Or heard a butterfly cry?
Have you ever played rummy with a pharaoh's mummy
Or snakes and ladders with a fly?
Have you skated on the ice with a family of mice
Or looked the Loch Ness Monster in the eye?
Have you ever heard a scarf give a hearty laugh
Or heard a bow-tie give a sigh?
Have you ever had a chat with a ginormous rat?
You haven't? Well, neither have I!

- John Foster   *Drawing - Shaz Jubeen*

MY HEADTEACHER

My headteacher
is a maniac.

She uses
the wrong side
of the road.

She parks
where she shouldn't.

She never signals.

I sometimes think
she shouldn't be allowed out
on that skateboard.

- Bernard Young   *Drawing - Chris White*

AN ELDERLY LADY PHONES THE POLICE STATION TO REPORT HER TORTOISE MISSING (AGAIN)

Someone has stolen my tortoise.
It really isn't right.
Someone has stolen my tortoise.
They took it away in the night.

Someone has stolen my tortoise.
He was five years younger than me.
Someone has stolen my tortoise.
He was only eighty three.

Someone has stolen my tortoise.
I'm worried they've nicked him to sell.
Someone has stolen my tortoise.
I'm going through tortoise hell.

Someone has stolen my tortoise.
They did exactly the same last year.
Someone has stolen my tortoise.
It's a shock when they disappear.

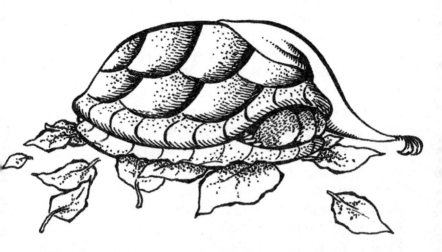

A POLICE OFFICER RESPONDS TO THE ELDERLY LADY WHO REPORTED HER TORTOISE MISSING (AGAIN)

No one has stolen your tortoise.
This happens every November.
No one has stolen your tortoise.
I've explained it before. Do you remember?

No one has stolen your tortoise.
And there's no need to come down the station.
No one has stolen your tortoise.
You're a victim of hibernation!

– Emma Purshouse   *Drawing - Sarah Fogg*

PINK

Pink, pink, I love pink!
Pink is the bestest colour, I think.
My pyjamas are pink, my duvet is pink,
My wallpaper's pink, my ceiling is pink,
My coat is pink, my shoes are pink,
My hoody is pink, my knickers are pink,
My lips are pink, my cheeks are pink,
My tongue is pink, my lunch is pink.
Pink, pink, I love pink!

Pink, pink, I hate pink!
Pink is the worstest colour, it stinks!
Pink is fluffy, pink is yucky,
Pink is vomity, pink is vile,
Pink is disgusting, an abomination,
Pink is the colour of a baboon's bum,
Pink is for girls, pink is for babies,
Pink is my idea of hell.
Pink, pink, I hate pink!

– Alan Durant

DON'T TICKLE TIGERS

Don't try and tickle a tiger,
Don't go and tangle his tail,
Don't try and trick him
Or tumble and trip him:
Your game will most certainly fail.

Don't even look at a lion,
Don't go and lie in his den,
Don't lollop after him,
Lick him or laugh at him:
That way your life's at an end.

Tigers and lions are dangerous,
So keep right away from their lairs,
And while we are talking Precautions:
The same goes for hippos and bears!

- Celia Warren   *Drawing - **Cat Reda***

THE MOUSE

One year we built a great big fire,
As big as any house,
And we were going to light it,
When I saw the little grey mouse.

It ran into a pile of wood,
A leaf hanging from its mouth,
But it wasn't a curling leaf it held,
It was a tiny, curling mouse.

In the middle of the bonfire
Lay a car tyre, round and flat,
The little grey mouse had only built
Its nest in the middle of that.

'Don't light the fire!' I shouted,
'Whilst a family's in its house.
We'll have to take the bonfire down
And save that little grey mouse.'

So we did. We took it all to pieces
And set the little mouse free.
We put its nest in our garden
In the shelter of a tree.

Then we lit the bonfire,
And flames lit up our house.
And shone on the home under the tree,
The house of the little grey mouse.

- Gwen Grant

MAKING A MEAL OF IT!

A canny schoolgirl from Dunoon
Explains, 'With a knife, fork and spoon,
Instead of chopsticks,
I could eat in two ticks
This way lunch takes me all afternoon!'

*Poem and Drawing **by Philip Waddell***

WARNING!

Do not lie
Do not lie on
Do not lie on a lion.

- Philip Monks

CWASANT

Or briosh.
I lik tham
with jam.
Yamy.
Ar yu
having see real?

- Philip Monks

DADDY DISASTER

He lives in a house that's all lopsided
Where the chores aren't done and the drawers aren't
tidied
His car is wrecked and his driving reckless
His favourite outfit is his breakfast
How did he get to become a father?
Ladies and Gentlemen - Daddy Disaster

The hand he lends is crammed with thumbs
One job to do's too much at once
Who broke the bath? Do you have to ask?
Can he fix it? No, he can't.
If you want to a make a mess then meet the master
Welcome to the world of Daddy Disaster

Who cut himself on a pencil sharpener?
Coloured his face in fluorescent marker?
Set his hair on fire with a harmless sparkler?
Sat his bottom down on a wet banana?
Yes, you must've guessed the answer
Ladies and Gentlemen - Daddy Disaster

- Justin Coe

*Drawing - **Brick***

MISTER RANDALL'S SANDALS

Mister Randall's sandals –
they're ancient and they're old
Battered, torn and tattered and always open toed
Weathered leather from whenever – they just look a
shambles
Don't look now, don't look down at Mister Randall's
sandals

Mister Randall's sandals – loved by C.S.I.
You can tell just where he's been and what he's done
and why
Evidence for all to see – all mystery untangles
There's history, geology – in Mister Randall's sandals

Mister Randall's sandals –
there's glue and drawing pins
Chewing gum and squished and squashed-up blue tac
moulded in
Buckles jingle jangle as the ancient thread untangles
Coffee stains and lunch remains on Mister Randall's
sandals

Mister Randall's sandals – lumpy, chunky toes
The toenails that he never cuts and the mould and
where it grows
Toadstools lurk in the dirt and the murk and mushrooms
grow at angles
Blink your eyes as the gases rise – Mister Randall's
sandals

Mister Randall's sandals – observe the yellow skin
But where do the sandals end and where do his feet
begin?
The skin and leather – joined together like waxy melted
candles
The leather's dried – the skin has died –
Mister Randall's sandals

Mister Randall's sandals – his hairy hobbit feet
The gases that they're giving off like rancid rotten meat
Fungus fumes foul every room as the stink takes hold
and strangles
Hold your nose when you're near the toes of
Mister Randall's sandals

Legendary, indestructible, everlasting, incorruptible,
fossilized, immortalised
Prehistoric, alas poor Yorrick, Biblical and mythical
Invented with the wheel, the comfort and the feel of a
well worn soul and heel of …
Mister Randall's sandals

– Paul Cookson   *Drawing* **- Nathan Ariss**

WHAT WOULD A DINOSAUR DINE ON?

What would a dinosaur dine on
if he came to our house for tea?

Would
burgers and chips
and ice cream and jelly
and Kentucky Fried Chicken
fill up his belly?

Or

Would he
raid our fridge
and our freezer?
Our cupboards?
Our larder?
Would he clean-out
the greenhouse
and gobble
the garden?

And
if he still wasn't
full after that,
would he
munch on
the goldfish,
the gerbils,
the cat?

Dinosaur Foot Note...

*It would be fairly safe to
invite a dinosaur to tea
as many of them were
herbivores
(plant eaters).*

*Although some of them
weighed as much as 100
tons so you may have
some problems with the
seating arrangements at
the tea table.*

Would he
chomp on
my sister
or my older brother?

Would he
chew up
my father,
crunch up
my mother?

AND THEN!
OH MY WORD!
WHAT IF HE…
WANTED A PUDDING
AND THE PUDDING
WAS ME!

Dinosaur Foot Note 2…

*Never invite
Tyrannosaurus to tea!
Tyrannosaurus Rex
everything!*

– Emma Purshouse

WOOZLING

We once went winter woozling
With a Japanese giraffe,
A muscleman from Mayo
Known as Millicent McTaff,
A pensioner whose wartime
Service had been in the WAFF,
And someone else who couldn't come
But sent a photograph.

We didn't have a purpose
But thought it might be a laugh,
So met up one wet Wednesday
By the Sunday cenotaph
To pen our own prospectus
Over coffees in a caff,
Then ordered jellied omelettes
And a tap-water carafe.

Their kitchen was a cricket-pitch
So food was quite a faff.
The chef put on a helmet,
Gave utensils to his staff,
And started bashing tables
Screaming "Get out of my gaff!
I porridge fish for foreigners
Not snacks for cheap riff-raff."

We gave up winter woozling
Which was good because it's naff.
It won't be calibrated,
Can't be plotted on a graph,
And, television's killed it.
You'll have read its epitaph,
Though some say that they've seen it
In the mountains of Llandaff.

– Nick Toczek

NOTHING UNDER THE BED

You think there's something horrible under your bed?
Like a monster or a snake or a bear?
And you can't get to sleep? Well, like I said
I looked today and found nothing there –
Except:

Chewing gum, crayons, a pizza box,
Fluff, books, comics, stinky socks,
Ten toffee wrappers, shoes, combs, hair,
Used sticking plasters, underwear,
Black mouse droppings (and mouse traps),
Sandwiches, spaghetti, straps,
Popcorn, rubbers, paper clips,
Marbles, magazines and chips;
Lucky charms and seaside stones,
Half chewed sweets and chicken bones,
Bottles, screws, nails, jars, jugs,
Elastic bands and earplugs,
Broken pencils, bracelets, braces,
     Spoons and string and old shoelaces . . .

So there can't be a monster or a snake or a bear
Because there wouldn't be room for them there.

- Eric Finney

GREEDY GREG

Greedy Greg was the messiest eater,
Mouth as wide as a fifty-four seater.
You'd never believe what he'd try to fit in;
Less like a mouth - more like a bin!

The sight of him eating would usually tend
To send both his parents half round the bend.
Not just the heaps but the way that he ate;
They'd work themselves into a terrible state.

"Don't slurp your soup whatever you do,
It sounds like you've got your head stuck down the loo.
Don't blow it cool, we won't tell you again,
You've drenched us both through with warm soupy rain!"

"And please close your mouth when you're chewing your food;
It seeps through your teeth - we've told you it's rude.
Oh why can't you eat with a knife fork and spoon?
You handle your food like a half starved baboon."

So it went on, "Elbows off the table,
Please slow down!" But the monster wasn't able.

Dad didn't know what to do - not a clue.
Mum wanted to cart him right off to the zoo.
Then a plan! A flash of inspiration,
A scheme that they thought would be their salvation.

They hired a skip and filled it with water
And boiled it all up in an hour and a quarter.
Then aided by men from the rugby club
They tipped in a ton of Greg's favourite grub.

Spaghetti, miles of it, the biggest dish ever.
Then carefully they knotted each strand together.
Then they laid their trap, the devious planners,
The scheme that they hoped would clean up Greg's manners.

"Come downstairs, Greg, it's time for tea!"
"Coming mum. Wow! Is all that for me?"
"Make yourself comfy here on the settee,
Take hold of this end and suck it and see!"

Greg sucked like a vacuum but even faster,
His mouth filling up with the great snake of pasta.

But then came the chair, it flew right in
Next came the table, the light and the bin,
The dog and the cat and the goldfish too.
His cheeks like rubber just grew and grew.

The carpet, the hoover, the grandfather clock,
His parents were turning quite pale with the shock.
The plan was to make Greg a better eater
But there he was munching the gas fire heater!

Soon all that was left were the walls and the rafters
And Gregory smiled, "Now what's for afters?!"

– Antony Lishak   *Drawing - Noel Ford*

A TALL GIRAFFE

I wish
I was
a tall giraffe
I'd chew
the tails of stars
and
if
the
earth
grew
far
too
loud
I'd
lift
my
head
into
a
cloud
far
far
away
from

this
world's
crowd
of
city
men
who
are
so
proud
of
traffic
fumes
and
cars

– Julie Boden   *Drawing - **Hunt Emerson***

TEDDIES ON TIPTOE

It's almost nearly the middle of night,
    the streets are dark with no-one in sight.
But in my bedroom which is messy and muddled,
    my teddies are hugged, my teddies are cuddled.

The clock says three, the moon is mumbling,
    the curtains curve, the clouds are tumbling.
But in my bedroom which is tangled and tatty,
    my teddies are bonkers, my teddies are batty.

An owl is hooting, the water pipes moan,
     a little green light on the top of the phone.
But in my bedroom which is comfy and cosy,
     my teddies are restless, my teddies are dozy.

The street is so quiet though a dog is growling,
     the urban fox is skulking and prowling.
But in my bedroom time slinks and slips slow,
     my toys are all sleeping, my teddies on tiptoe.

- John Rice   *Drawing* **- Clive Goddard**

LOW FLYING RABBITS AHEAD

Watch out for obstreperous elephants
Or fidgety fleas in your bed
There's a bear on your chair –
don't stare! Beware
Low flying rabbits ahead

Be warned! Argumentative aardvarks
And the tigers haven't been fed
When in doubt you must shout,
There be dragons – watch out!
Low flying rabbits ahead

Caution – cantankerous catfish
There's a dodo called Fred in the shed
And the mad fortune teller says,
Take your umbrella
Low flying rabbits ahead

– Roger Stevens   *Drawing - Ryan Taylor*

PET HATES

Come on in! Don't mind Rex,
he's very tame, you'll see.
Sit down. Oh, look! Rex likes you,
his head is on your knee.

Yes, I've worked hard to train him
since he hatched out of his egg.
Rex can fetch, and walk to heel,
roll over, sit, and beg.

He loves his tummy tickled,
he never goes out straying.
Well yes, he bit my arm off,
but he was only playing.

He's licking you? He licks me, too.
Don't worry, Rex adores us.
You want to know what breed he is?
He's a Tyrannosaurus.

Don't run away! He'll think you're prey,
he can smell your fear.
Bad boy, Rex. That's playing rough.
Down, Rex! Down!

Oh dear.

- Jane Clarke   *Drawing - **John McCrea***

THE SPACEMAN

He thinks he is a spaceman
So he's wearing a tinfoil suit
He's even got a gun that blows bubbles
And a shiny silver sabre, to boot.
He thinks he is a spaceman
He jumps off the dining room chair
He thinks he is a spacemen
He's just making me pull my hair
He eats food that's lumpy and bumpy
He sleeps upside down in a tree
He moonwalks across the garden
Bounces on my trampoline with glee
He thinks he is a spaceman
Jumping up to the moon and the sun
But clearly it's just Dad's desperation
His way of avoiding my Mum.

- Steph Dale

*Drawing - **Hunt Emerson***

BODY BEAUTIFUL

My eyesight is weak, my eyebrows are scorched,
my heart doesn't beat, nose shines like a torch.
My hands are all shaky, eyes flicker and blink,
my ears are gigantic, chin shaped like a sink.

My hair is like seaweed, my nostrils are hairy,
my cheeks like pancakes on the face of a fairy.
My mouth hates lollies; my tongue can't lick any,
my lips are red worms and my neck is all chickeny.

My shoulders are crooked; my eyes are like eggs,
my elbows are knobbly, my arms like lamb's legs.
My chest's like a fishpond, my tummy oceanic,
my back is zigzaggy and my bum fryingpanic!

My thighs are like puddings, my knees are broken,
my calves are floppy and my soles are soaken.
My ankles are angled, my shins are mellow,
my feet are like puddings, my big toes are yellow.

- John Rice   *Drawing - Andrew Chiu*

MISTLETOE KISSING

Standing under mistletoe
is embarrassing, you know:
girls come up and kiss your cheek,
aunties hug you till you're weak,
cousins slurp until you wriggle,
sisters peck, then go and giggle.
Granny's poodle, Hercules,
slobbered over both my knees.
Worst was when my brother Jake
gave me a smacker by mistake.

From now on I'm sure of this -
I'll give the mistletoe a miss.

- Jill Townsend   *Drawing - Simon Woolford*

IF

If you can keep your head when all around you
Are losing theirs and tripping over you
If you can find a home when none has found you
And claim their garden, house and bedroom too
If you can wash a mile from any water
And roam without recourse to any map
Unwind from cold and calculating slaughter
By curling on a warm and cosy lap:

If you can fall, and find your feet by falling
If you can sleep, yet keep a watchful brain
If you can wake the dead with caterwauling
Or die yourself, and live to die again
If you can stare for minutes without blinking
And wear for hours on end a dreamy smile
And seem to think - quite undisturbed by thinking -
Through narrowed eyes aglow with secret guile:

If you can make one heap of shredded paper
From magazines put safely out of reach
And sigh, and sulk, and claw and madly caper
At all attempts to reprimand or teach
If you can force your bleary-headed owner
To let you in and out the door at dawn
And oscillate from socialite to loner
And stare back in again with face forlorn:

If you can walk on shelves and spare the china
Ignore commands but answer to your name
If you can hog the whole of a recliner
Designed to hold the largest human frame
If you can turn to stone for half a minute
And climb a tree in fifteen seconds flat
Yours is the blackbird, nightingale and linnet,
For - after all - you are a cat. My cat.

- Nick Green   *Drawing - **Jane McGuinness***

HAIR SO LONG SONG

What the world says,
I don't care.
I just want to
grow my hair.

Let it grow
while I sing this song :
Come on there,
grow really long.....

Grow right down
till you reach the ground,
then I'll wrap you
round and round,

Wrap you round
my chest and tum,
warm my torso,
snuggle my bum,

Wrap you round
my legs and feet,
back to my head
then all's complete.

Tie a knot
right there on top.
Keep away
from the barbershop.

Out in the cold,
out in the storm,
I don't care,
I'm really warm.

Off goes the storm,
out comes the sun.
Phew, I'm hot!
This ain't no fun.....

Shouted HELP!
and the barber called.
Look at me :
I'm bare and bald!

- Tony Mitton   *Drawing - **Sarah Fogg***

THE KITCHEN IS A JUNGLE

The kitchen is a jungle
Where savage beasts live
In the shadows of the cupboard
And the dark of the fridge.

Spaghetti winds and curls and snakes
Across the jungle floor
The hungry kettles screeches
The mighty oven roars.

The potatoes are watching you
With half-closed earthy eyes
Onions bare their vicious fangs
And scream their high-pitched cries.

You're a hunter in this jungle,
And you're following the track,
Of the rarest of its creatures -
The grinning fresh cream cake.

- David Calcutt　　　　　　　　*Drawing - Tim Harries*

CONKERS

"Don't throw sticks at the trees," my Mum said,
"Only hooligans do that!
If that stick falls on someone's head,
It could knock them flat!"
That's what my Mum said.

"Don't be in such a rush," my Mum said,
"Just wait until they fall."
But waiting was no good.
The hooligans with bits of wood
Just came and got them all.

Once, I was standing by the tree
At the corner of our street,
When the biggest one you've ever seen
Fell right down at my feet!

I wasn't doing anything –
The tree just sort of dropped it.
I haven't got it any more…

I swapped it.

- Sandra Horn   *Drawing - **Chris White***

MABEL'S UNSTABLE

Mabel's unstable, be careful, beware
Of that look in her eyes that says, 'I don't care.
I'll do what I want, however unfair.'
Mabel's unstable, and isn't all there.
Mabel's unstable, and able I'm sure
To nail up an angel on to the back door.
Somebody must take her far, far away.
That's what we long for, and pray for each day.
No one remembers from where Mabel came.
Found on the doorstep and brought in from the rain
She sat in a corner, glowered and moaned,
'I was raised by a man whose head was horned.'

Mabel's unstable and if you want proof
Look down at her foot. You'll find only a hoof.
Her eyes are ablaze, like cinders, like fire,
And her dark hair is tangled like razor-sharp wire.

- Brian Patten

Drawing *- Sammy Borras*

RUDOLPH KNOWS

In his red soccer shirt, Rudolph the fan
Was off to the match when his wife said, "Look, man,
It's snowing, the game may be off, what a pain!"
Said her husband, "My dear, that's not snow, it's just rain."
So to settle the matter they went out together
To turn up their faces and study the weather.
"You were right, it is rain," pronounced Rudolph's wife,
"The game will be on you can bet your sweet life."
Her husband replied, "Yes, it is rain, that's clear –
And Rudolph the Red knows rain, dear."

- Eric Finney

TEACHER, TEACHER

Teacher, teacher
If you can't find Sue
She's in the cloakroom
Looking for her shoe
Teacher, teacher
If you can't find Ben
He's in with the Head
'Cos he's late again
Teacher, teacher
If you can't find Hans
He's still in the shower
'Cos he's lost his pants

- Roger Stevens   *Drawing - Mikey Ball*

OUR BABY IS HOWLING

Our baby is howling,
it just isn't right,
Winston howls and he howls
all day and all night.

He howls at his sister,
he howls at his brothers,
he howls at their friends,
and at their friends' mothers.

He howls when he's wet,
he howls when he's dry,
Winston howls and he howls,
and he doesn't know why.

He howls at his Mum,
and he howls at his Dad.
The howling, the howling,
it's driving us mad.

At last! Winston settles.
It's a special day.
Is Winston changing?
Will he be okay?

Winston is changing!
We stand and stare
as our baby stops howling,
and starts...

                 ... growing hair.

Hair grows on his fingers,
hair grows on his toes,
hair grows on his ears
and all over his nose.

Look at his teeth!
Look at his nails!
Winston's so happy,
he's wagging his tail.

Outside, shadows shift
in the silvery gloom.
As the clouds roll away,
Winston howls at the moon.

Yes!
Winston's got it!
He's got it right!
We only howl
when the moon's full and bright.

Our baby's a werewolf,
just like me and you.
Let's join in the howling
A-oo-ooo,
oooo-ooooo-oooooooooooooooooooo!

- Jane Clarke

*Drawing - **Laura Howell***

ABSENT

Dear Teacher,
my body's arrived
it sits at a table
a pen in its hand
as if it is able
to think and to act
perhaps write down the answer
to the question you've asked

but don't let that fool you.

My mind is elsewhere.
My thoughts far away.

So apologies, teacher,
I'm not here today.

– Bernard Young   *Drawing - Ryan Taylor*

HOW TO BUILD YOUR OWN UNIVERSE

If you think that science is dreary
try this lovely Big Bang Theory.
If you're bored or at a loss
why not build your own cosmos?

First you need an empty space
infinity long is just the place
then you simply have to scatter
a millions tons of cosmic matter.

Make some atoms very small
'til you can't see them at all.
Next stir in a trillion masses
of functionally inert gases.

Then you merely have to glue
up a zillion stars or two.
Next you sprinkle in the mix
The Laws of Thermodynamics.

Now to start your planetry motion
what you need's a big explosion.
Crash and smash! Ka-bing! Ka-boom!
Let it rip! There's lots of room!

That really got your worlds revolving.
Look right there – that's life evolving.
Count you still have all your spheres
then cool for thirteen billion years.

Now you have to find a spot
for a very special pale blue dot.
Make it lush with lots of greenery
add some oceanic scenery.

After that you're nearly done
Just light it with a massive sun.
Now you've finally given birth
to a baby planet – name it Earth.

- Ian Billings   *Drawing - **Hunt Emerson***

*Drawing - **Roger Penwill***

YOUR MUM'S A TOMATO

Your mum's a tomato, your dad is a bear,
Your auntie's a dustbin with brown curly hair.
Your brother's an egg that went SPLAT! on the floor
And your sister looks just like a small dinosaur.
SO WHAT?

Your mum is a lemon, all sour and with pips,
And your dad's a giraffe with brown spots on his hips
Your grannie's a hedgehog with a prickly coat
And your sister's a weasel or maybe a stoat.
SO WHAT?

Your mum is so fat she can't get through the door
Your kid brother's so scrawny he'd fit in a drawer.
Your cat has got fleas and your sister's got mumps
And your great-uncle Harry's all hairy, with lumps.
SO WHAT?

Your grannie eats slugs for her dinner and tea
And she barks like a dog when she goes for a wee
Your brother's got pimples, your sister's got nits
And your mum drives a car that is falling to bits.
SO WHAT?

If our mums are all weird and our dads are all dim
And our sisters are freaks and our grannies are grim
Then we must be like them, but that isn't true.
For I know I'm FANTASTIC... just like you.

- Enid Richemont

OKAY FOR DAD

If dad burps and doesn't say pardon,
If he picks his nose,
If he laughs at a rude joke on the telly,
It's okay
But if it's me … mum tells me off

If dad speaks with his mouth full,
Or falls asleep when my boring auntie's here,
If he leaves his Brussel sprouts,
It's okay
But if it's me … mum tells me off

It's okay for dad …
He can bite his nails and poke about in his ears,
Leave his coat and shoes in a heap
At the bottom of the stairs in the hall,
Fall asleep with his books and papers all over the floor,
Forget to do the washing up (on purpose),
Sit and pick his toe nails with a fork,
Play his music at full blast with the telly on at the same time
Or spend three quarters of an hour in the bathroom
With a newspaper and a cup of tea
And mum never ever says anything to him
But if it's me … she tells me off

And one day,
When I grow up to be big
I'm going to be just like my dad.

- Paul Cookson

DIAMONDS

Twinkle twinkle little star
Don't give me none of dat
Up above the stars so high
I'd rather stroke da cat
Dimonds! Now your talking
You didn't mention those!
Up above the sky so high
Sparkles like to boost my clothes.
Twinkle Twinkle little star
That is so like going to be me
Strutting my way along the street
Like a cool celebrity.
Twinkle twinkle little star
You say it's just a rhyme
O man, what a downer
Did you have to waste my time?

- Steph Dale   *Drawing - Laura Howell*

(VARIATIONS ON INCY WINCY SPIDER)

Incy Wincy spider
climbing up my shoe
counting my laces
1 and 2.
When he sees the big foot
the spider gives a shout
scurries to the corner
and climbs back up the spout.

Incy Wincy spider
dancing on the sun,
ski-ing over Pluto
shouting, "This is fun!"
Surfing on his website,
Weaving hyper-space.
Hiding in a black hole
from all the human race.

- Julie Boden   *Drawing - Mikey Ball*

GOT THE HUMP

Gran says
if she were a witch
she'd turn our cat
(who's grumpy
always got the hump)
into a camel.

I'd like that
no-one else
in our street
has a camel-flap

- Joan Poulson

THE GOLDFINCH

The goldfinch flies across the pond,
A speck of beating gold that brushes by.

The goldfinch flies across the pond,
A rush of glitter in the green surround.
A touch of breath, a golden sigh.

The goldfinch rests across the pond,
A fleck of beaten gold that brushed me by.

How carelessly can nature's gold be found.

- Philip Monks   *Drawing - **Gemma Sheldrake***

THIS IS WHERE...

...I learnt to be.
And this is where I learnt to read,
and write and count and act in plays,
and blossom in so many ways...
And this is where I learnt to sing,
express myself, and really think.
And this is where I learnt to dream,
to wonder why and what things mean.
And this is where I learnt to care,
to make good friends, to give, to share,
to kick, to catch, to race, to run.
This is where I had such fun.
And this is where I grew and grew.
And this is where? My Primary school.

- James Carter

TEN THINGS YOUR PARENTS WILL NEVER SAY TO YOU

Let's forget dinner tonight, we'll drink beer instead.

Goodnight children, I'm off to bed.
Take the car wherever you want.

No homework tonight! I'm putting all homework
in the fireplace immediately.

Children, don't be so quiet.
Start yelling, turn the TV up, start arguing, now!

Yes, of course you can have twenty-one of your friends
come over on Saturday night. We've got heaps of room.

No, don't listen to the dentist.
Chocolate and biscuits are good for your teeth.

Yes, that SuperDoopaComputerGame is too expensive,
but let's buy it anyway and put it in your room.

What's that? You broke the kitchen window. Good boy!

Can someone go to the shop for a newspaper?
Here's £100 - keep the change.

Yes, I know today is Monday, but let's stay home from
school anyway.

- Steven Herrick

DOOR

Dad took our front door
Back to the hardware store
He was angry, in a fit
"Why bring back your door
to our hardware store?
It's odd I have to admit!"

"I brought this door
To your hardware store,
I'm so angry I could spit,
I brought back this door
To your hardware store,
'cos somebody's already opened it!"

- Ian Billings   *Drawing - **Hunt Emerson***

THE FLURROCK

Deep in the forest of Netherford Knoll
all hidden by bracken and mist
lives a creature so secretive, timid and rare
that it might not even exist.

The flurrock, they say, is a bit like a mole
or it might be a bit like a boar,
but as nobody's actually set eyes on one,
no one can say for sure.

How big is is a flurrock? Again, no one knows,
but it hides in the briars and gorse.
So it's probably slightly bigger than mice
but not as big as a horse.

Some say it has fur and feathers and scales
and it sheds its skin every week.
While others insist it has little webbed feet
and horns and a long curved beak.

It might live on leaves and lichen and moss
or sausage and salad dressing.
Some scientists say it eats flies and jam
but at best they're only guessing.

It's a creature of perfect camouflage,
elusive, unseen and rare.
So how, you ask, can we say for sure
that the flurrock is actually there?

The answer lies in the flurrock's poo
which is vivid and luminous green.
So although you can't see where it is,
it's easy to see where it's been.

*Poem & Drawing by **Clive Goddard***

CYBER

There's a bully in the bedroom
                    and he wasn't there before,
There's a bully in my pocket
                    and he's rotten to the core.
There's a bully breathing heavy
                    takes me to a scary place,
Spits threats, writes toxic lies,
                    does it with a smiling face.
He's no wider than a match box,
                    fits snug inside your hand,
There's a bully in the bedroom
                    and he comes from Cyberland.
Has no fists or bloody knuckles,
                    he won't punch you in the lip,
The hurt happens in a text when
                    he lets a swearword slip.
He demands your dinner money,
                    join a gang or carry knives,
Race hate or name-calling,
                    cyber bullies taking lives.

There's a bully in the wardrobe
                    yet the key is in the lock,
And they go to the same school,
                    they live on the same block.
But they hurt you from a distance
                    and they murder on the phone,
Or they'll plug in a computer
                    bringing nightmares to your home.
There's a bully finger twitching,
                    sends abuse and fear and hate,
Pull the plug, switch them off,
                    tell someone, it's not too late.
There's a bully in the bedroom,
                    feeds off silence through a mouse,
Spreads poison through a screen,
                    takes you prisoner in your house.
Talk and Tell, open up
                    - don't keep it bottled in,
Talk and Tell, open up
                    - don't let the cyber bullies win.
Exterminate - Exterminate
                    - STOP!

- Terry Caffrey

BORED

I'm kicking a ball
I'm kicking a ball
I'm kicking a ball against a wall

I'm bored
I'm bored
I'm bored I'm bored I'm bored

I'm banging my head
I'm banging my head
I'm banging my head against a wall

Hey! there are some girls
Hey! there are some girls
Hey! look over there   (where?)
There are some girls

I'm dribbling the ball
I'm heading the ball
I'm bouncing the ball back off the wall

I'm cool
I'm cool
I'm cool I'm cool I'm cool

Hey! there go the girls
Hey! there go the girls
Hey! there go the girls
The girls have gone

I'm kicking a ball

I'm banging my head

I'm bored I'm bored I'm bored

- Bernard Young   *Drawing - Ellie Cummins*

LIGHTWEIGHTS

Night falls
and bumps its head.
Its eyes are heavy,
it's going to bed.

The sun rises
like a kite
'cos daytime's lighter
than the night.

- Jill Townsend

BOB

There was once a useless explorer called Bob,
Who wasn't cut out for the job.
He would suck on his dummy,
And cry for his Mummy.
Then just sit around and sob.

- Gez Walsh   *Drawing - Hunt Emerson*

ALLIGATOR TERMINATOR

Don't be deceived
By the alligator:
His favourite food's
Not mashed potato.
In slimy swamps
Near the equator,
It waits – it is
A patient waiter –
And sometimes soon,
And sometimes later
It spots an innocent
Spectator:
In this case, it's a
Girl called Greta,
A video camera
Operator.
Trying to film
The alligator,
She slipped in mud.
Some seconds later,
Her friend, a TV
Commentator,
Did his best
To extricate her.
To no avail –
The 'gator ate her.

Take careful note:
The alligator
Is definitely
A terminator.

*- **Eric Finney***
*Drawing - **Hunt Emerson***

NEVERSAURUS

When dinoasurs roamed the earth,
So huge it was easy to spot 'em.
You'd frequently see a triceratops,
But never a tricerabottom.

- Celia Warren   *Drawing - John Crawford*

LOOK AT ME!

Gosh, it's all so exciting!
Look how far away the ground is!
Look at the sky!
Look how near it is!
I can touch it! I can touch it!!

I'm high up in the treetops!
The branches are like thin pineapples!
The leaves are like green skateboards!
The birds are circling and calling "Way to go man!"
"Way to go!"

Here comes the wind! Watch out tree!
Watch out me!
I'm not scared!
See the clouds running away! Ha! Ha!
Silly, scaredy clouds!
Look at me!
I'm riding the wind! Wheee!
I'm a tree-climbing, skateboarding wind-surfer!

I'm as light as a leaf! I'm on the wind!
I can feel myself floating out from the tree!
I'm on my leaf skateboard!
I'm going out from the tree!
I can ride this wind!!!

Uh-oh
!
!
!
!

- Philip Monks   *Drawing - Will Dawbarn*

I really should warn you, before I begin
This story won't fill you with glee.
It's a tale of depravity, horror and sin,
Called:

'THE MONKEYS AND MR. McDEE.'

Just round the corner, behind the estate
There's a building most people ignore.
There's only one human who goes there, but, wait,
There are Monkeys – ten thousand or more.

Or rather, there used to be, up to last night,
When the blighters said they'd had enough.
It took courage, but they weren't afraid of a fight,
Because one little monkey was tough.

For years the poor monkeys had toiled like slaves,
At levers, at pulleys and pistons.
But sometimes their friends disappeared – without
graves,
While the rest were too scared to ask questions.

Then one little monkey, the smallest of all,
Grew tired from working all day.
So he sat in the corner and took out a ball,
Then casually started to play.

Suddenly there was a crash, then a creak,
And the monkey jumped up from the floor.
His teeth were a-chatter, his knees had gone weak.
He was standing above a trapdoor.

This monkey was tired, but he was alert,
As the floor where he stood slid away.
He was so small he skipped off it, unhurt,
With an elegant paso doblé. *(That's a type of dance, by
the way. Monkeys are especially good at it. Something
about their knees...)*

A moment too late he remembered his ball.
He watched as it rolled down the hole.
The monkey was shocked when he saw his toy fall
Between jaws, which swallowed it whole.

A crocodile lived under the factory.
There it was: sharp-toothed. Mean. Underfed.
Everyone there was a crocodile-snack-to-be.
The thought filled the monkey with dread.

Then, with a rumble as big as the first,
The trapdoor slid back into place.
In all his short life, this day was his worst,
And the horror contorted his face.

'So that's what's been happening to all of my friends,'
Thought the monkey, with tears in his eyes.
'They worked all their lives and then met sticky ends,
No time for farewells or goodbyes.'

Then he took a deep breath and called out 'There's a
beast
Under the factory floor!
It dines every day on a monkey-shaped feast!
So stay calm and proceed to the nearest door.'

Everyone panicked! They all ran amok,
But the littlest said 'It's up to me.
If I don't do something about this, we're stuck!
I'll tell the boss: Mr McDee.'

He steadily mounted the wrought iron stairs.
Each step made him more of a wreck.
He ran his hand over the quivering hairs
That stood up on the back of his neck.

At the top he knocked on a solid oak door,
And looked down on the monkeys, heart drumming.
Their fate was below them, under the floor.
Then a bad tempered voice said, 'I'm coming.'

The door creaked open, and there was the boss,
Who sneered through his teeth, 'Well, what is it?'
As he turned and sat back at his desk, looking cross,
'To what do I owe this visit?'

'There's a crocodile under the factory floor,'
Said the monkey to Mr McDee,
'And the workers are worried to work any more,
We're frightened - especially me.'

Mr McDee maintained his calm air
For of course he had nothing to hide.
But he shifted a bit in his fat leather chair
And smiled before he replied:

'There's a crocodile under the factory floor?
Well there's nothing much that I can do.
You'll have to work harder than ever before,
I suppose. Especially you.'

'But under the factory floor is a pit!
My machine's a trapdoor in disguise!
And it's just big enough for a monkey to fit.
I've seen it with these very eyes.'

'Get out!' screamed Mr McDee, 'That's enough!
You've wasted too much of my time.
I don't have to deal with such trifling stuff,
I assure you the croc is benign.' *('Benign' means 'sweet
and innocent and would never eat a monkey'. How can
he say that?! Is he crazy? Is he lying?! Something's
definitely going on here and I don't like it!)*

The monkey ran back to the workers' enclosure,
Where nobody knew what to do.
The rest of the monkeys had lost their composure.
Oh, what a hullabaloo!

The crying and shouting was echoing round
And around each diabolic machine.
Oh what a horrible, horrible sound.
Have you ever heard monkeys scream?

But on top of the biggest machine was our friend,
Silently standing alone.
He picked up a tube to speak into the end,
And voilà – one ape megaphone.

He may have been small, but his voice was well aimed,
Crystal clear and fortissimo.
'It isn't the crocodile's fault,' he proclaimed,
'The monster's above, not below!'

'We've been had,' he went on. 'This is monkey abuse.
We work, but what is it we make?
Eternally toiling but not to produce?
This infernal factory's fake!

'What does he think? That monkeys are thick?
We're here, but what are we for?
Mr McDee's pulled a dastardly trick:
We're crocodile food - nothing more!

'It's time to rise up! It's time we were freed!
It's high time our tyrant was sacked!'
By now all the factory monkeys agreed,
They were angry, and ready to act.

'That Mr McDee – it's all his fault!'
They cried as they ran through the hall.
And leading the charge, to direct the assault,
Was the bravest, but smallest of all.

They swung from the levers like good monkeys should.
They threw down their spanners with pride.
When they reached McDee's door, they pounded the wood.
In minutes, they'd made it inside.

With three or four monkeys to carry each limb,
They lifted the evil dictator.
They'd suffered too much. They wanted him
To be faced with a mean alligator.

Mr McDee was kicking and screaming,
Which, until now, no monkey had seen.
'This is revenge for your terrible scheming,'
They told him. 'Now work that machine.'

'This is madness,' cried Mr McDee in his shock,
'I'm quite at the end of my tether.
I admit it – I need you to feed to my croc.
When they eat chimp they make the best leather.'
*(Woah! He's admitted it! He keeps crocodiles to make
leather and he only keeps the monkeys to feed to the
crocodiles! I hope it all goes wrong for him now...)*

Now, Mr McDee should have known not to stay
Where he stood without working, but blew it.
Coz then the trapdoor in the floor slid away
And poor Mr McDee, he fell through it.

Too big for the hole, McDee wouldn't fit,
So a plunger came down from the ceiling
And stuffed the man into the reptile pit,
All the time writhing and squealing.

Down he went, but such a short fall
That the monkeys could watch as he cowered.
For below them McDee was curled up by the wall
Of the cell. He was slowly devoured.

The monkeys were free! Every last one!
They tore down their pulleys and levers.
Then they ran through the streets - a new life had be-
gun!
And they sang: la revoluçión, viva! *(I threw in a bit of
Spanish for you there. Did you notice? Did you like it? I
don't really know what it means, but my friend told me it
was something like: 'Long live the revolution!')*

But our brave monkey said 'Stop running away!
There's one more thing we have to do.'
Then back to the factory he flew, shouting 'Hey,
Let's rescue the crocodile too!'

He bellowed below, 'Here I am, crocodile,'
And he freed the beast underneath!
There was no danger now in the crocodile's smile,
But bits of McDee in his teeth.

The crocodile laughed - the monkeys had won!
Mr McDee had been beaten!
While everyone else broke into a run,
The crocodile walked. *(He'd just eaten.)*

Nobody knows where the slave monkeys went,
Some say they'll never survive.
And the chance might be just one per cent they're content,
But they're free – and that means they're alive.

I've spoken and heard and seen terrible plights,
As terrible as they could be.
But many have suffered no more than was right.
Especially Mr McDee.

'That's nonsense!' you'll say, 'All this happened last night?'
'One monkey set the rest free?!'
It happened. I know. I was there. That's right,
The brave little monkey was me.

- Joe Craig

FABLE

At writing Aesop was tip top
But his limericks, alas, weren't much cop
His first lines were fine
And his rhymes were divine
But he just didn't know when to stop
And always wrote a little moral on the end.

- Roger Stevens

A FIT OF THE SULKS

I'm really mad. I'm going to sulk
For longer than ever before.
I could easily go on sulking
For a week – or even more.

Yes, longer than a week!
A week's not long enough
To demonstrate to everyone
That I'm really in a huff.

I'll go on sulking for a month:
These sulks will not fade fast.
I might just keep it up all year:
These sulks are going to last.

. . . .

Trust Mum to spoil my sulky plan.
She smiles, says, "Hello, Flower.
Recovered from your sulks yet?
They usually last an hour."

- Eric Finney

HOPPING MAD

I was happy as a froggy
in my smelly, stagnant pool.
I was one jump ahead.
I was free! Life was cool.
I got to move from pad to pad –
it really suits a bloke
to live a happy froggy life
until the day you croak.

I was happy as a froggy,
and the froggy life I miss,
ever since that stupid Princess
gave my froggy lips a kiss.
I'm a handsome Prince now,
but it doesn't make me glad –
I was happy as a froggy,
so it makes me hopping mad!

- Jane Clarke   *Drawing - **Cat Reda***

SAD DAY

Today is

A sad day
A dark day
A bad day
A grey day.

A bleak day
A weak day
An itchy day
A wearing something scratchy day.

A broccoli day
A rainy day
A something in
my eye day.

An off day
A lemon day
A nothing in
My tummy day

A porcupine to touch day
A creeping down the stairs day
A whisper to my bear day
A dark day, a sad day

A please give me a hug day.

– Julie Boden

HAPPY DAY

Today is a good day
A yellow day
A golden sparkling silky day.

A smile day
A play day
A let's jump up and sing day.

A chocolate day
A strawberry day
A birdsong all day long day.

A cuddling your pet day
A never to forget day
A feeling like a Queen day.

A warm glow in my tummy day
A 'Look how good you've been!' day
An everybody loves you day

A yellow day
A shining day
A good to be
Alive day.

– *Julie Boden*

TIDINGS

I found a bottle on the beach
Beneath the seabirds' twitter –
It had this message corked inside:
Dispose of – do not litter!

*Poem & Drawing **by Philip Waddell***

RAINBOW CLOUD

Tommy was a little lad
feeling very glum
What made Tommy feel so bad?
He hadn't got a chum.

"I have no special buddy
I can call my own
To play football, to get muddy
And catch balls I have thrown."

This problem troubled Tommy
Wrapped around him like a shroud
His whole life seemed cast over
by a grey and looming cloud.

Tommy grew lonelier
the anger in him sprouted
It made him frown and curl his lip
When kids came near he shouted.

He hit the boys, he kicked the girls
He even stuck out his tongue
Other kids kept away
"The way you behave is wrong!"

Tommy's black cloud darkened
His life now seemed so grim
His loneliness was ten times worse
And no one would speak to him.

One dreary Wednesday morning
The sky began to clear
Tommy saw a beautiful sight
which gave him a bright idea.

From beneath the thundery blanket
The sun began to shine
And a rainbow reached across the sky
making Tommy feel very fine.

"Perhaps there is a rainbow
In the cloud inside my head
How can I blow the cloud away
And make the sun shine instead?"

He saw a boy called Marley
Kicking a ball all alone
Tommy smiled and he shouted
"Here mate, you can't play on your own!"

Marley grinned and chipped the ball
Then came all the others
Peter, James and Darren
Big Jack and the McGirr brothers.

The game took off fantastically
And many goals were scored
Tommy was having so much fun
No longer was he bored.

The boy who had spent so much time
Sulking by the gates
Was now "Bending it like Beckham"
And playing with new mates.

Tommy brought about this change
And made him very proud
He'd made his own rainbow
Shine from a dreary cloud.

However big your problem
However dark your night
Remember that inside yourself
Your rainbow cloud shines bright.

- Fi Gallimore   *Drawings - Lew Stringer*

SAUSAGE MAN

The strangest man I've ever heard,
when he can't think of any word
doesn't fret and scratch his head,
he just says sausages instead.

If he forgets the word for car
he drives a sausage near and far.
In the shower, what shall he do?
A sausage can replace shampoo.

If umbrella slips his brain
he'll raise a sausage in the rain.
When he can't remember rose
he'll hold a sausage to his nose.

He forgets about the chair?
He'll sit upon that sausage there.
Has the table skipped his mind?
He'll use a sausage, you will find.

The sausage stories never end -
and be prepared if he's your friend;
for if your name escapes him too,
he'll make a sausage out of you.

- Alison Chisholm

*Drawing - **John McCrea***

MY DOG'S FIRST POEM

(to be read in a dog's voice)

My barking drives them
up the wall.
I chew the carpet
in the hall.
I love to chase
a bouncing.........banana?
Everywhere I leave
long hairs.
I fight the cushions
on the chairs.
Just watch me race
right up the............shower?
Once I chewed
a stick of chalk.
I get bored
when the family talk.
Then someone
takes me for a ....wheelbarrow?

- Wes Magee   *Drawing -* **Nathan Ariss**

CHOCOLATE LABRADOR

We were going to get a pet,
a chocolate Labrador!
Mum said it would be great
but me, I wasn't so sure.

She could see that I was worried
so I told her how I felt,
that I'd rather have a real dog
because a chocolate one might melt!

- Emma Purshouse   *Drawing* *- Jane McGuinness*

PARENTS' EVENING

Parents' Evening at our school:
Dad was bound to act the fool.

First of all he didn't know
who my teacher was and so
he joined the queue to see Miss Lee
who said she'd never heard of me.

When at last he found Miss Rolf
he bored her, talking about golf
and telling her about when he
was at the school. Never mind me.

In the car park there was worse.
Dad put the car into reverse.
He turned it to avoid a hump
and there was an almighty bump:

he'd dented someone else's car -
"Ah, Headmaster - there you are!"

- Jill Townsend

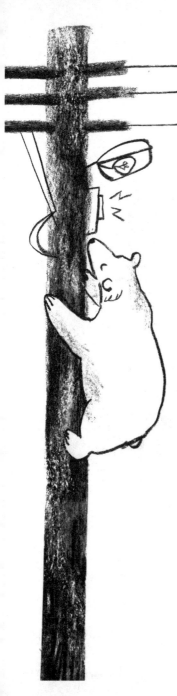

BRUIN'S MISTAKE

Bruin loved honey
And he thought he heard a bee,
So he climbed up a pole
That he took for a tree.

The buzzing got louder
As Bruin climbed higher,
But he found no bees,
Just a telephone wire.

- Celia Warren
Drawing - Jane McGuinness

SNOTTY SPOTTY

I once had a spot on my nose,
Well who hasn't had one of those?
It caused such a fuss,
When it exploded with puss.
So they washed me down with a hose!

- Gez Walsh   *Drawing - **Tim Leatherbarrow***

DON'T TELL SIR

A teacher was puzzled why one
of his lessons was causing such fun,
but continued the day
in his usual dull way,
with the zip of his trousers undone.

- Trevor Parsons

THE BUDGIE LIKES TO BOOGIE

The budgie likes to boogie,
the budgie likes to rock.
He wakes us every night
when he rocks around the clock.

The budgie likes to jive,
to spin around, to twirl.
His body full of rhythm,
his head is in a whirl.

The budgie boogie-woogies
along the table top.
The budgie disco dances,
the budgie likes to bop.

He's just about the best
and his moves are really neat.
You should see the budgie boogie,
you should see his flying feet!

In front of the dangly mirror
he plays his air guitar.
The budgie likes to boogie,
the budgie is a STAR!

- Brian Moses   *Drawing - Brick*

DOG TRAINING

Doggone it! Who would think a boy would be so hard to train?
They say his breed's intelligent, but my boy has no brain.
I've tried to teach him doggy ways since I had him as a lad.
He's a loving, loyal friend, but he makes me barking mad.

When he was a baby, I thought he'd turn out right,
he crawled around upon all fours and often howled at night.
He gulped his food and slobbered. I was sure he couldn't fail,
but his teeth stayed blunt and stunted and he never grew a tail.

He doesn't beg, or lift his leg against a tree or pole.
He drinks from taps and never laps out of the toilet bowl.
He sits on chairs, he sheds no hairs, he doesn't chew his wellies,
he goes on strolls, but never rolls in anything that's smelly.

My boy isn't up to scratch. I don't wish to be blamed
I'm doggedly determined to get him properly trained.
He's got to learn to change his ways. He's broken every rule.
But I think I have the answer…
and that's Dog Training School!

- Jane Clarke   *Drawing - **Noel Ford***

THE DAY THE ROPE SWING BROKE

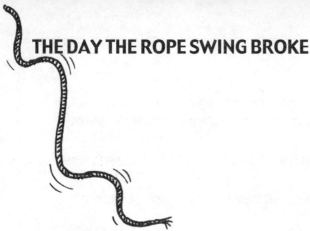

I'm glad that it was not my go
High and low and to and fro
Above the water down below
The day the rope swing broke

I'm glad that I was high and dry
I'd be a liar to deny
I laughed enough to make me cry
The day the rope swing broke

I'm so glad he was the one
Much too heavy to get on
A moment later he was gone
The day the rope swing broke

A rush of air and then a splatter
Feel the mud and water scatter
It serves dad right for being fatter
The day the rope swing broke.

- Paul Cookson
Drawing - Hunt Emerson

TOGETHER NESS

Bashful Ness,
Timid Ness,
Coy Ness,
Shy Ness,
Address?
Loch Ness.

*Poem & Drawing by **Philip Waddell***

ONE DAY DOWN AT THE BEACH

Down at the beach one hot, sunny day,
Mum and Dad dozing, the children at play.
A day free of stress, a day with no hassle,
until they spotted a cow on a bouncy castle!

Springing so high almost touching the roof,
a big sofa cushion tied to each hoof.
Two rows of teeth as yellow as corn,
a layer of bubble wrap covered each horn.

The cow took a tumble, a topple and trip,
her tail lashing out like the flick of a whip.
Her legs splayed out, gave a shudder and quake,
that's how she invented the famous milk shake.

Down at the beach one of those sunny days,
the parents were baffled, the children amazed.
They had seen something odd, like a surprise parcel,
they had spotted a cow on a bouncy castle!

- John Rice   *Drawing -* ***Ellie Cummins***

DOOBY DOOBY DOOB

O dooby dooby dooby
O dooby dooby do
I love to shooby-wooby
Especially with you

I like the way you do it,
So dooby wooby noo
You put your body through it
So nooby shooby roo

O dooby dooby dooby
O dooby dooby dooo
O dooby dooby dooby
O dooby do be quiet.

- Matt Harvey   *Drawing -* **Sammy Borras**

COUSINS

Every evening
when the dark creeps in
like a smothering black cape,
our little family
~ Mum, Dad, Brother, Sister, Gogo the cat and me ~
we get together to huddle and cuddle
and keep us each safe.

Every night
when the moon rises like a white saucer,
our little family
~ Mum, Dad, Brother, Sister, Gogo the cat and me ~
go to bed in our warm rooms.
We tuck each other in
and sleep safe in green dreams.

But in another land,
when the same dark creeps in,
a broken family in a wild wind
looks to the same moon, red and angry,
and each makes a wish,
~ Mum, Dad, Brother, Sister, Asmara the stray dog ~
all ask for food, for medicine, for peace, for rain.

Just these, only these, do our beautiful cousins ask for.

- John Rice

THAT FLY

That fly that's quietly twiddling away
In the sugar bowl down there:
It's not washing its hands, you know,
Or applauding, or saying a prayer.
Before it flew in through the window
It was doing what house flies do
Such as squatting on rotting rubbish
Or cowmuck or maybe dog poo . .
And now it's on your sugar bowl!
And it's doing exactly what?
Well, it isn't eating your sugar –
No, it's much nastier than that.
Down its mouth tube it's squirting saliva,
Making pools all gloopy and gummy,
Then it's sucking the puddles back up again –
There's only one word for it: yummy!
It's a sticky-sweet feast for a house fly –
And next it might land on your plate
To practise its twiddling and squirting there
So the plan is: Exterminate!

- Eric Finney

SPLURT
GLOOP
GULP

*Drawing - **Tim Leatherbarrow***

GOODBYE CRUEL WORLD

I've lost my nerve, I'm losing my voice,
my heart has been stolen by Jane,
I've given a hand to a stranger
and my face has just fallen again.

My legs have shot out from under me,
my arms have been grabbed from behind,
I've lent my ears to some Romans
and I'm rapidly losing my mind.

My bottom's been pinched, and my teacher
has taken quite enough of my cheek -
if I carry on going at this rate
I'll be gone by the end of the week.

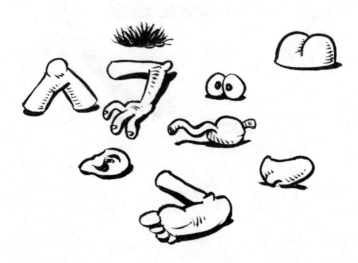

- Trevor Parsons   *Drawing - **Hunt Emerson***

JOSIE GROWS UP

Imagining a bike for a baby spider,
with a shiny bell on each of its three handlebars,
or a ghost trap made of bubble bath bubbles.
Wanting to be a crocodile when she grew up.
Saying 'dilodaph', 'hurt-ed' and 'fall-ed',
'At drinks time I kiss-ed Jake,'
and 'We laughed our breath out.'
Passing a tattooed madman with a huge gut
And pointing and shouting
'That dad's going to have a baby!'
Thinking girl pirates should have their own flag:
Pink velvet with a sparkly sequin skull and crossbones.
Watching grisly wildlife on TV and saying
'Death wasn't one of God's best ideas.'

- Paul Dowswell

THE GOONJO

Wow! It's a very rare "Goonjo"!
A bird written of in folklore!
Look - it's half goose and half banjo!
I've never seen one before!

She'll open her beak and make twangy sounds,
This one looks in perfect health!
So if we're lucky we may just see
this creature pluck itself!

*Poem and Drawing by **Chris White***

THE MONSTER

I'm a monster in my world
Of shivering shadows and oozy weeds.
In my homemade armour
And my stony boots
I crunch across the pondbed
And the whole world shakes!
My jaws can break
The earth in two.

Look out! I'm coming to get you!

I'm the terror of the pool
With its hidden trapdoors and secret caves.
In my horrible mask
With its hungry grin
I hunt the silent jungle
For anything that moves.
Is there something to eat
Up there too?

Watch out, you lot! I'm coming to get you!

- David Calcutt

WE'RE LUCKY

We've five-a-day. We've veg. We've meat.
We've bread and toast because we've wheat.
We've sugar cane and sugar beet
To make our drinks and puddings sweet.
We've always got a snacky treat.
We choose. We share. We don't compete.

We're lucky.

We've water in the summer heat.
We've fridges full of things to eat
So finding food is no great feat.
We dine until we're full, replete.
We've cosy rooms. They're clean. They're neat.
We don't sleep on an old groundsheet.

We're lucky.

We've clothes to wear, shoes on our feet.
Our crops don't fail. Our sheep still bleat.
We've got no yearly drought to beat.
We don't have warfare on the street.
We are not fleeing in retreat.
We don't face death, despair, defeat.

We're lucky.

– Nick Toczek